398

The Pedaling Man

The Pedaling Man

and other poems by Russell Hoban

drawings by Lillian Hoban

New York

W · W · Norton & Company · Inc ·

BY RUSSELL HOBAN WITH

ILLUSTRATIONS BY LILLIAN HOBAN

The Pedaling Man

The Mouse and His Child

Save My Place

Goodnight

The Little Brute Family

The Stone Doll of Sister Brute

The Story of Hester Mouse

Bedtime for Frances
  (*illustrated by Garth Williams*)

Bread and Jam for Frances

Baby Sister for Frances

The Sorely Trying Day

Herman the Loser

The Song In My Drum

Text Copyright © 1968 by Russell Hoban
Illustrations Copyright © 1968 by Lillian Hoban
First Edition
Library of Congress Catalog Card No. 67–18682
All Rights Reserved
Published simultaneously in Canada by
George J. McLeod Limited, Toronto
Printed in the United States of America
2 3 4 5 6 7 8 9 0

FOR PHOEBE,

who listens to what the wind says.

Contents

Author's Note

Time tries constantly to take the world away from us, and in the end, of course, it does. Any poem is the writer's attempt to hold on to what world he has and to grab a little more if he can. I think that good poems help the reader do the same thing, and so become necessary to him.

I needed to tell about Skilly Oogan and the place my youngest daughter calls Anfruca. I needed to tell about the one star blotted out by a broken kite, about the sea gull's eye, and about the dog named Clock. It isn't possible that everybody will need all of these poems. But if some of my readers need some of my poems, I'll be satisfied.

Russell Hoban
—January, 1968

To Walter de la Mare
1873–1956

His words in pasture safely sing
With grazing sheep,
Or dark in owl-lit belfry swing
Where demons sleep;
And sometimes like Great Paul they ring
With hugely quivering bronze to bring
Bright angels standing on each roof,
And to each window startled truth.

What the Wind Said

"Far away is where I've come from," said the wind.
"Guess what I've brought you."
   "What?" I asked.
"Shadows dancing on a brown road by an old
Stone fence," the wind said. "Do you like that?"
   "Yes," I said. "What else?"
"Daisies nodding, and the drone of one small airplane
In a sleepy sky," the wind continued.
   "I like the airplane, and the daisies too," I said.
   "What else?"
"That's not enough?" the wind complained.
   "No," I said. "I want the song that you were singing.
   Give me that."
"That's mine," the wind said. "Find your own." And left.

The Crow

Flying loose and easy, where does he go
Swaggering in the sky, what does he know,
Why is he laughing, the carrion crow?
Why is he shouting, why won't he sing,
How did he steal them, whom will he bring
Loaves of blue heaven under each wing?

The Sparrow Hawk

Wings like pistols flashing at his sides,
Masked, above the meadow runway rides,
Galloping, galloping with an easy rein.
Below, the fieldmouse, where the shadow glides,
Holds fast the small purse of his life, and hides.

Skilly Oogan

Skilly Oogan's no one you can see,
And no one else can be his friend but me.
Skilly lives where swallows live, away up high
Beneath the topmost eaves against the sky.
When all the world's asleep on moonlit nights,
Up on our roof he flies his cobweb kites.
He has an acorn boat that, when it rains,
He sails in gutters, even down the drains.
Sometimes he hides in letters that I write—
Snug in the envelope and out of sight,
On six-cent stamps he travels in all weathers
And with the midnight owl returns on silent feathers.
In summer time he rides the dragonflies
Above the pond, and looks in bullfrogs' eyes
For his reflection when he combs his hair.
And sometimes when I want him he's not there;
But mostly Skilly Oogan's where I think he'll be,
And no one even knows his name but me.

One Star Less

Alone, and stirring lightly in the night,
What is there quite as quiet as a broken kite?

What silence is so silent as its whisper
In the highness of its fall? It roosts among
The branches, blotting out a star; it bears
The rains and mornings, every dawn
Till it is gone—

It is May; the hem of evening rustles as she
Walks beside the pond, the songs of peepers
Whispering like circlets at her ankles, clashing
Tiny gongs and bells; the stars
Dance in the water—
All but one.

The Pedaling Man

We put him on the roof and we painted him blue,
And the pedaling man knew what to do—
He just pedaled, yes he pedaled:
He rode through the night with the wind just right
And he rode clear into the morning,
Riding easy, riding breezy, riding
Slow in the sunrise and the wind out of the east.

A weathervane was what he was—
Cast-iron man with a sheet-iron propeller, riding a
Worm gear, holding a little steering wheel,
Iron legs pumping up and down—show him a
Wind and he'd go. Work all day and
All his pay was the weather. Nights, too,
We'd lie in bed and hear him
Creak up there in the dark as he
Swung into the wind and worked up speed,
Humming and thrumming so you could
Feel it all through the house—
The more wind, the faster he went, right through
Spring, summer, and fall.

He rode warm winds out of the south,
Wet winds out of the east, and the
Dry west winds, rode them all with a
Serious iron face. Hard-nosed, tight-mouthed
Yankee-looking kind of an iron man.
"Show me a wind and I'll go," he said.
"I'm a pedaling fool and I'm heading for weather."
The weather came and he kept on going, right into
Winter, and the wind out of the north and no letup—
We lived on a hill, and wind was what we got a lot of.

Then a night came along, and a blizzard was making,
Windows rattling and the whole house shaking,
But the iron man just hummed with the blast,
Said, "Come on, wind, and come on fast,
Show me your winter, make it nice and cool,
Show me your weather—I'm a pedaling fool!"
Gears all spinning, joints all shivering,
Sheet-iron clattering, cast-iron quivering till WHOMP!
The humming stopped, and we all sat up in bed with
Nothing to listen to but the the wind right through into morning.

And there he was when we dug him out, propeller all bent,
One eye in the snow and one eye
Staring up at the sky, still looking for weather.
He never let on he was beat, not him.

Well, my father put him up on the roof again, this time
Without the propeller.
"Let him ride easy," he said. "A man can only take
Just so much north wind, even if he's iron."

Small, Smaller

I thought that I knew all there was to know
Of being small, until I saw once, black against the snow,
A shrew, trapped in my footprint, jump and fall
And jump again and fall, the hole too deep, the walls too tall.

The Empty House

Where the lone wind on the hilltop
Shakes the thistles as it passes,
Stirs the quiet-ticking grasses
That keep time outside the door,
Stands a house that's gray and silent;
No one lives there any more.

Wending through the broken windows,
Every season and its weather
Whisper in those rooms together:
Summer's warm and wandering rains
Rot the leaves of last year's autumn,
Warp the floors that winter stains.

In a papered hall a clock-shape,
Dim and pale on yellowed flowers,
Still remains where rang the hours
Of a clock that's lost and gone.
And the fading ghost keeps no-time
On the wall it lived upon.

On a stairway where no footsteps
Stir the dusty sunlight burning
Sit the patient shadows turning
Speechless faces to the wall
While they hear the silent striking
Of that no-clock in the hall.

"Dawn of no-time! Noon of no-time!"
Cries the phantom echo chiming,
And the shadows, moving, miming,
Slowly shift before the light.
But no eye has seen their motion
When the clock says, "No-time night!"

No eye has seen them dancing
In their blackness fell and bright,
To a silent tune
In the dark of the moon
When the clock sings no-time night.

Typo

"Nitgub," said the typewriter,
And clenched the paper tight.
"Nitgub positively.
It is here in black and white."
"Nonsense," I said.
"I typed N-O-T-H-I-N-G;
The word, of course, was *nothing,*
Simply nothing, don't you see?"
"Nothing may be what you meant,
But *nitgub's* what you wrote.
I like it," said the typewriter.
"It strikes a happy note.
It has more style than *nothing,*
Has a different sort of sound.
The color is superior;
The flavor's nice and round.
Have you plumbed its deepest depths,
Its mystery explained?"
"All right," I said, "I'll take it.
Nitgub ventured, nitgub gained."

London City

I have London, London, London—
All the city, small and pretty,
In a dome that's on my desk, a little dome.
I have Nelson on his pillar
And Saint Martin's-in-the-Fields
And the National Portrait Gallery
And two trees,
And that's what London is—the five of these.

I can make it snow in London
When I shake the sky of London;
I can hold the little city small and pretty in my hand;
Then the weather's fair in London,
In Trafalgar Square in London,
When I put my city down and let it stand.

Esmé on Her Brother's Bicycle

One foot on, one foot pushing, Esmé starting off beside
Wheels too tall to mount astride,
Swings the off leg forward featly,
Clears the high bar nimbly, neatly,
With a concentrated frown
Bears the upper pedal down
As the lower rises, then
Brings her whole weight round again,
Leaning forward, gripping tight,
With her knuckles showing white,
Down the road goes, fast and small,
Never sitting down at all.

Katya Plays Haydn

Katya's fingers on the keys
Long and limber take their ease.
Katya's feet beneath the chair
Dangle gently in the air.
Harmony loves to abide in
Katya's knees and Joseph Haydn.

The Tin Frog

I have hopped, when properly wound up, the whole length
Of the hallway; once hopped halfway down the stairs, and fell.
Since then the two halves of my tin have been awry; my strength
Is not quite what it used to be; I do not hop so well.

Solu the Barber

I know a barber named Solu.
The words he speaks are soft and few;
He nods to me and says hello
Because his place is where I go
For haircuts now.

With comb and scissors through the day
He works, then puts his tools away,
Cleans up the shop, sweeps up the hair,
Sits down in his own barber chair
And rests awhile.

He takes down from its little shelf
A small guitar he made himself
And while the city evening brings
Its lamplight to the street he sings
Of islands far.

I know him just to say hello
But not quite well enough to go
Inside to listen to his song,
So on the street I linger long
Outside his door.

Sometimes I sit across the way
Not close enough to hear him play,
But in the lighted window there
I see him singing in his chair
With his guitar.

His lips move while his fingers strum
And soft beneath my breath I hum
And wonder to what tropic harbor
On music sails Solu the barber.

Islesford Shore

Past sea-worn stones, wild roses, and the swallows skimming,
Past warblers singing in the wild pear,
Past two crows walking on the beach and no one swimming,
Past spruce and fir-trees, puttering slowly where
A line of sunpoints dances on the ebbing tide,
The lobster boat comes; sea gulls on it ride,
And one bird, perching on the stubby mast,
Revolves his head to see the land go past.

Old Man Ocean

Old Man Ocean, how do you pound
Smooth glass rough, rough stones round?
Time and the tide and the wild waves rolling,
Night and the wind and the long gray dawn.

Old Man Ocean, what do you tell,
What do you sing in the empty shell?
Fog and the storm and the long bell tolling,
Bones in the deep and the brave men gone.

Maine Sea Gulls

Two gray-winged farmers of the sea, they ride
The drowsing summer wind to reap the tide,
And as they go they slowly squawk together,
Chatting as farmers do about the crops and weather.
"I look for rain," says one. "Wind's in the east."
"Clamming's been poor," his friend says, "but at least
The herring's coming in across the bay."
"Ayeh," they both agree, and flap away.

The Sea Gull's Eye

The thing about a gull is not the soaring flight, the creaking cry;
The thing about a sea gull is its eye—
Eye of the wind, the ocean's eye, not pretty,
Black at the center of its yellow stare, no pity
And no fear in it, nor reason, nothing warm
To shelter its own wildness from the storm—
Naked life only, disdainful of its form.

Along the harbor road the other day
I found a broken sea gull where it lay
Great-winged and skyless, wrecked by stone or shot—
Some boy, perhaps, had done it who had not
More pity than his prey
And there it lay
And lived awhile, until that yellow eye
No longer looked out on the ocean sky,
And life, indifferent to boys with stones,
Flew up again with crows that picked the bones.

The Friendly Cinnamon Bun

Shining in his stickiness and glistening with honey,
Safe among his sisters and his brothers on a tray,
With raisin eyes that looked at me as I put down my money,
There smiled a friendly cinnamon bun, and this I heard him say:

"It's a lovely, lovely morning, and the world's a lovely place;
I know it's going to be a lovely day.
I know we're going to be good friends; I like your honest face;
Together we might go a long, long way."

The baker's girl rang up the sale. "I'll wrap your bun," said she.
"Oh no, you needn't bother," I replied.
I smiled back at that cinnamon bun and ate him, one two three,
And walked out with his friendliness inside.

Tea Party

The teapot's full, the cups are clean,
The cloth is white, the grass is green,
The jam is sweet, the cakes are good,
The sunlight smiles as sunlight should;
But only crickets sing with me,
And only shadows drink my tea.

I know a word that no one knows;
I know a place where no one goes.
If sometime, in the smiling sun
(When all the cricket songs are done,
And shadows all have drunk their tea)
A friend should come to visit me,
I'll show the place where darkness bites,
And speak the word the silence writes.

Anfruca

(AN-FROO′KA)

When I go to Anfruca (which is very, very far–
Too far for a bicycle, too far for a car)
I always take a bucket and I always take a spade,
For we may be gathering sponges and we may be digging jade
In Anfruca where I go
(Near the crow).

In Anfruca there are oogans and they live among the trees,
And some of them are all of them; they do just as they please.
They wheel their wheelbarrows in the wheelbarrow races
And they always carry bookmarks so they never lose their places
In Anfruca where I go
(Near the crow).

That's where Charlie Everybody and his brother spend the summer
With a lightning bug to read by and a bullfrog for a drummer.
They march with all the oogans when they do Anfrucan walking
And they spell out words in pebbles so the crow won't hear them talking
In Anfruca where I go
(Near the crow).

Do you know how the crow
Always knows
When he goes
To his house how to go?
Well, he knows he must go
Through Anfruca (fast or slow)
Till he sees the name of Crow.
Now you know.

Home From the Carnival

Gone all the lights and all the noise,
Gone all the cotton candy's joys,
And all my money spent and gone
With all the rides I rode upon
And all my money gone and spent
Upon the tables in the tent:
The Wheel of Fortune clicked and spun—
I lost my dimes and nothing won,
Not even from the bottom shelf.
I bring home nothing but myself,
And take to bed with meager cheer
The teddy bear I won last year.

School Buses

You'd think that by the end of June they'd take themselves
Away, get out of sight—but no, they don't; they
Don't at all. You see them waiting through
July in clumps of sumac near the railroad, or
Behind a service station, watching, always watching for a
Child who's let go of summer's hand and strayed. I have
Seen them hunting on the roads of August—empty buses
Scanning woods and ponds with rows of empty eyes. This morning
I saw five of them, parked like a week of
Schooldays, smiling slow in orange paint and
Smirking with their mirrors in the sun—
But summer isn't done! Not yet!

Boy With a Hammer

He'd found some lumber from an old fence rotting
By the woods, and raised it up,
And said it was a fort that he was making,
But the blue jay, knowing better, cried out, "Thief!"
Because the urgent hammer, fast and fierce,
Was nailing the October day to woodsmoke and
The birches and the wind;
Now it was his to keep—the boy's and not the jay's,
His day for good and all, and so
The outraged bird cried "Thief!" and flew
To find his own day in some other place.
The boy worked as the wind blew colder and the day grew long;
It was his fort, he said, and he would make it strong.

Winter Ducks

Small in the shrink of winter, dark of the frost and chill
Dawnlight beyond my window sill,
I lace the morning stiffly on my feet,
Print bootsteps down the snowy hill to meet
My ducks all waiting where the long black night
Has iced the pond around them. With a spade
I break the water clear; the hole I made
Restores their world to quacking rhyme and reason—
Tails up, they duck the lowering, gray-skied season,
Heads down, they listen to the still-warm song
Of silted leaves and summer, when the days were long.

Hound And Hunter

Well, I had a dog, and his name was Clock,
And the sound he made was Tick Tick Tock Haroooo!
And we hunted minutes in the daytime thickets,
In the hills of night and the songs of crickets,
And he howled at the moon, Haroooo!

And I wound him up with a big brass key,
And nobody knew his name but me,
For he slipped in and out of the empty spaces
Where the shadows live who have no faces,
And he bayed the hours in a voice of black,
And he barked and he belled as he kept the track
Of the days that ran with their ears laid back.
Good boy, Clock! Hark to Clock! Haroooo!

And he licked my hand when the hunt was done,
And he sniffed at the smell of my smoking gun,
And he trotted home with his tail held high,
And he howled the moon down out of the sky, Haroooo!

Then he learned to run without the key,
And he changed his hunting, and hunted me.

And he hunted me out of childhood's thickets
To the fields of dawn and silent crickets,
And he bayed on my trail with his voice of black,
And I ran, ran, ran, but he kept the track
Til I left the fields and swam the river
To the other side, where I stand and shiver
With my clothes all wet, and my clothes too small,
For I've grown too old, and I've grown too tall,
And I'll never go back again at all.

And far away on the ridge of day
I can hear him bark, I can hear him bay,
And I hear another hunter say,
"Good boy, Clock! Hark to Clock!" Haroooo!

Index of First Lines

About the Author and the Illustrator

Russell and Lillian Hoban have jointly produced more than twenty books for children, including *The Mouse and His Child, The Story of Hester Mouse, Save My Place, Goodnight,* and the popular "Frances" books—*Baby Sister for Frances, Bedtime for Frances* (illustrated by Garth Williams), and *Bread and Jam for Frances.* Mr. and Mrs. Hoban live in Wilton, Connecticut.